Too High!

Written by Judy Nayer
Illustrated by Madelaine Gill

"Get the balloon!" said the frog.

2

"I can't," said the duck.
"It's too high!"

So the balloon went by.

"Get it!" said the cow.

"I can't," said the hen.
"It's too high!"

So the balloon went by.

"Get it!" said the lion.

"I can't," said the bear.
"It's too high!"

So the balloon went by.

"It's not too high for me!"
said the butterfly.

"Good-bye!"

8